Why neural rewiring is crucial for full recovery

What is neural rewiring?

How does your brain become "wired" in the first place?

Learned reactions

Learned emotions

Learned words

Learned actions

Learned thoughts

Learned belief systems

Changing beliefs for recovery

Where does your brain get its data?

How what you pay mental attention to influences your brain

Practical application?

Redirects

Stages of identification and rewiring

Super-highways

Rewiring Examples

Rewiring your fear of not suppressing your bodyweight (fear of weight gain)

Rewiring negative body image

Rewiring negative body image actions

Rewiring negative body image emotional reactions

Rewiring the feelings of wrongdoing after eating differently

Rewiring fear of unrestricted eating (body trust and communication)

Tabitha Farrar

Rewiring food judgement (learning to eat honestly)

Rewiring compulsive movement

How long does rewiring take?

PROLOGUE

When I finished writing *Rehabilitate, Rewire, Recover!* (RRR!) I vowed I would never write another book. I figured I would never have to, because RRR! is so bloody long and I'd hoped if I wrote a brick that I would be done. Turns out I'm not.

When the idea for this book came into my head I had a bit of a tantrum and sulked for a couple of days. Matt asked me what was wrong. I told him, *"I have to write another bloody book."* *"Oh, shit,"* he said. *"I'm sorry."*

"Oh, shit" indeed.

It's not that I don't like writing. I love writing. It's the editing that does me in. The editing process turns me into a hermit crab. It takes over every waking moment of my day and won't leave me alone. I don't like who I am when I am writing a book. I can't concentrate on anything else and I start waking up in the middle of the night with chapters in my head.

So, this time, I made a deal with myself. If my brain has decided, without my consent I might add, to make me write another book, this time I have conditions. It will be short. So short you can fold it up and fit it in your back pocket. No more bricks. I will only edit if there is a cat on my lap. I will have a never-ending supply of Cadburys at my desk. And tea, of course.

The success of RRR! in the year since I have published it has overwhelmed me. It is a testament to how the eating disorder community is now looking to and listening to people such as myself with lived experience: experts by experience.

This book is an addition to RRR! I already wrote 125,000 words on nutritional rehabilitation and neural rewiring, and RRR! is complete on its own. This book is focused just on neural rewiring, a more illustrated guide. This book doesn't just describe what neural rewiring from an eating disorder is, and how to do it; it is about how it *feels*. My hope for this book is that people in recovery feel guided and supported by it, but I have also written this for parents, family, loved ones, caregivers and treatment professionals who do not have first-hand lived experience of rewiring from a restrictive eating disorder. My hope is that if support systems can understand what rewiring entails, how detailed it needs to be, and what it feels like, they can provide compassionate and empowered assistance.

This book is for anyone with restrictive eating patterns and/or negative body image. And I'll remind you that you can have a restrictive eating disorder in any size body. I must thank my clients for gifting me with the experience that enabled me to write RRR! and, now, *Neural Rewiring for Eating Disorder Recovery*. Every client I have ever worked with has further taught me that the human body is a wonderful thing, and the less we meddle with our biology and try to force ourselves to be what we are not, the healthier we are.

I'll try and keep it under 15,000 words. Cheers.

WHY NEURAL REWIRING IS CRUCIAL FOR FULL RECOVERY

Of course, I'll have to explain a couple of things that I have already stated in RRR!, and the first one is this:

Full recovery = nutritional rehabilitation + neural rewiring

Nutritional rehabilitation is the process of getting the body out of energy deficit. It means that you fully achieve your unsuppressed bodyweight, your energy debt gets paid off, your body restores and repairs the damage incurred by malnutrition, and your genetic response to food scarcity fades out as your body and brain relax out of the perception that food is scarce.

Nutritional rehabilitation is vital for your recovery. You will not fully recover while you remain at a suppressed bodyweight. You can't get fully physically or mentally healthy if your brain believes that food is scarce. Nutritional rehabilitation, however, is not the complete story. You have to rewire the neural pathways of learned behaviours, actions, emotions, reactions and thoughts that years of having an eating disorder have established. You must both nutritionally rehabilitate and neurally rewire. Focusing on nutritional rehabilitation alone will keep you alive (which is a wonderful thing), but without neural rewiring, your chances of *fully* recovering from a long and enduring eating disorder are slim. Changing the learned behaviours, thought patterns and belief systems that your time with an eating disorder established is crucial.

WHAT IS NEURAL REWIRING?

I'm not a neuroscientist. I'm a person who has recovered from her own entrenched eating disorder, and who worked as a recovery coach for hundreds of others. I am an expert by experience, not by theory. Here is my definition of neural rewiring:

"Establishing freedom" is the result of the process of altering neural pathways. Challenging these established neural pathways is the change agent, and like all change agents it is bloody difficult. Like anything that is bloody difficult, it is much easier once you really understand it — once you have a feel for it. And this is what I want this book to help with: the practical application.

I asked the recovery community what they considered neural rewiring to be, and here are some of the hundreds of responses I got:

Full neural rewiring is when the knee-jerk reaction to stress isn't restricting my eating.

I understand it as reconfiguring my brain so that I don't carry out restrictions or old negative ED habits.

Reprogramming the brain out of ED habits.

Creating new, healthy patterns in my daily life in terms of eating and OCD ED rituals. Creating a new normal.

It's about training our brain to think differently! The best analogy I have is to think of your current thought pattern as a well-trodden path; it's easy to find and navigate, and feels comfortable and safe. To create a new pathway takes time and effort, there's no clear obvious way, you must make the path yourself, you don't know where you are going or where it will end up but you just have to keep going and trust the process. Over time, your well-trodden path will become overgrown and slowly disappear, and your new pathway will eventually become easy to use and feel as comfortable as your old one once was.

By doing healthy behaviours, eventually the brain gets comfortable doing these things even though it's hard at first. Essential to defeating an ED.

Brain plasticity in which new synapses are created or activated as a result of learning new behaviours, or deactivation of an area because of amputation or lack of sensory input.

A way to retrain your brain's thought patterns and beliefs. I kind of compare it to the physical body: if you are using some muscles incorrectly (for example, causing you to hunch your neck forward or something like that). This is causing you neck pain and maybe headaches. Maybe you go to PT. And you get exercises and you retrain your muscles to hold your head in a more anatomically correctly aligned position. You keep working on constantly reminding those muscles to keep your head in the correct alignment. After working on this for a while, you don't have to use so much conscious effort to keep that alignment. It happens more automatically because you have created muscle memory and strengthened those muscles that holds your head up. I feel it is the same for rewiring. The more you redirect your thoughts and challenge behaviours, the easier it will be. You retrain your "brain muscles" to work in a different way.

Neural rewiring is retraining your brain to respond in a different way than what is typical for you when presented with stimuli.

I also asked people in recovery to state what they would want treatment professionals to know about neural rewiring. Here are a few of many responses:

That it is very important in recovery. When I developed anorexia for the first time, my treatment team only focused on weight gain. As a result, I did not fully recover. Two months after discharge I relapsed. This time around (10 years later), I am focusing on neural rewiring and I believe that this time I will recover.

That it can still need doing after weight restoration and that it is important. That you sometimes feel just as bad when you're weight restored if you haven't rewired.

Takes time, but with persistence and proper nutrition it can work and help with permanent change.

It's a long and difficult process, and just because someone has managed to eat and gain weight, it doesn't mean they've managed to neurally rewire, and that means a weight-restored person may well keep living out their rituals and relapsing, or yo-yoing in and out of dangerous dieting behaviour.

That it is not just about food at all — my thought patterns and restrictive behaviours seep into EVERY aspect of my life, from sleep and movement to the way I tie my hair back that day, or the socks that I choose to wear.

That one of my biggest fears is that I will be 'forgotten' before I have fully gotten rid of my eating disorder thoughts.

Also, I know how to eat. I have a rational brain that knows how much butter to put on a piece of bread and how much milk to have in my coffee — I don't need to be taught this. It is actually allowing myself to do this that is the problem. I need practical, rational advice on how to get through each day without panicking and hating myself.

That it's actually the main part of recovery ... Recovery isn't recovery without it. 'Recovery' without the mental rehabilitation is just weight gain, which is just 'not dying'.

How does your brain become "wired" in the first place?

Your brain is always watching and learning. Everything you do. Everything you say. Even the thoughts that you pay attention to are being watched by your brain. Creepy, huh?

It really is like somebody's watching you the whole time. But worse, they are learning from every move you make. You know the way that if you have a toddler in the room you try not to swear, make rude jokes, or say certain things because you don't want them to pick up those habits or words? Well, you should be a bit like that with your own brain. Like a child, your brain is absorbing everything you do. It is taking it in. Logging it, and learning. I know this sounds a little backwards, because most of the time we think that our brains are just there giving us information. We sometimes forget that they never stop watching and taking it all in too.

The way your brain thinks today –– the way you react to things, your beliefs –– they are all learned. And for the most part, you did the teaching!

LEARNED REACTIONS

Okay, so say you develop an eating disorder. You suddenly go from having a regular, non-emotional reaction to food to having a freak-out if someone mentions a sandwich. That's pretty typical with an eating disorder. The trouble is, every time you have a freak-out, your brain is watching. It is logging that freak-out, and it is learning that freaking out must be the appropriate reaction to being offered a sandwich. Then, every time you react that way, you are providing your brain with data to support the notion that being offered a sandwich should provoke a stress reaction. The more you engage in that freak-out reaction, the stronger it becomes. Now consider this goes on for years. By the time you come around to wanting to do recovery, you have a hard-wired freak-out response to a sandwich.

LEARNED EMOTIONS

Your brain can learn that certain situations call for certain emotional states. In that sandwich example, years of freaking out about a sandwich will teach your brain that a sandwich is a threat. Why? Because you have been acting as if a sandwich *is* a threat. Because you have gone into the fear reaction so many times when being faced with a sandwich, after a while the fear emotion becomes the default, go-to emotional state that your brain will suggest is relevant when it sees a sandwich. In the same way, your brain learned that puppies = squee! your brain learned that sandwich = argh!

Learned emotional reactions are happening all the time in your responses to situations. Nothing our brain suggests as an appropriate reaction is written in stone. Just because an emotional reaction is a learned response doesn't make it "right" or "wrong." Understanding this is fundamental to developing the skills needed to choose which emotions you opt to participate in, and which you don't.

LEARNED WORDS

One of the brilliant ways our brains automate things to make life easier for us is by forming neural pathways to connect commonly associated situations with words. For example, if someone asks you how you are, you probably reply with *"fine"* or *"I'm well"* without giving it much thought. The word association games you may have played at some point are based on neural pathways. Say the word *"red"* and your brain has already linked up with a word or thought.

For me, when I had anorexia, my default words when offered food would be *"no thanks."* Years and years of always saying no to food meant those words became hard wired. My mouth would form them automatically. I had already said *"no"* or *"I'm not hungry"* at the anticipation of being asked if I wanted anything to eat.

Alongside the word *"no"* there was an associated physical feeling of irritation that became linked to the situation of being offered food. I physically recoiled away from whoever had offered. Even the way I would say *"no"* in that situation was specific. It was a sharp, don't-you-dare-mess-with-me, and very final, no. Always.

I had many default words and phrases. *"Black please"* for coffee (I don't like coffee, but I used to drink it when I had anorexia because I can tolerate black coffee better than I can black tea). *"The dressing on the side please,"* for ordering salad in a restaurant, or *"without the cheese"* for a Caesar. When I was in recovery I had to bite my tongue. These phrases were so automatic they were out of my mouth before I had even considered them most of the time, so I would often have to counter them, which was probably confusing to wait staff. *"Black coffee, please,"* then, nervously, ... *"Actually, I'll have a hot chocolate with cream."*

LEARNED ACTIONS

On being offered food, I would usually try to escape any pressure to eat by removing myself from the situation. Leaving the room. Getting up from the table. Excusing myself to go to the toilet if the conversation turned to food. Suddenly remembering I had another appointment I had to be at, or that I needed to make a phone call. Yes, I would often fake talking to someone on the phone, and pretend I had been called in for an emergency shift cover at work. The phone thing became a bit odd. I am sure other people noticed that I always seemed to get a phone call and had to be somewhere else should the conversation turn to getting food.

Leaving, whatever way I achieved it, became the auto-response. Sometimes I was already walking away, or reaching for my phone, before I had really had the chance to think about what I was doing, where I was going, or what I even wanted from life.

Another example of a learned action or response, due to my ridiculously competitive compulsive movement problem, was that if someone else moved, I had to move. Okay, this is where I start to sound like a complete lunatic, but stay with me. An easy example is watching a film. If someone else got up and went to the loo, or went into the kitchen to get something, I also had to move at least the distance that they moved. I hated this compulsion and would feel rage towards whoever had moved for "making" me have to move. It felt automatic after a year or so. Someone got up and I was on my feet before I'd thought about it. This was an incredibly weird and irritating learned action.

Standing on public transport was another learned action. It began as a conscious decision initially; whenever I was on a train or a bus, I would stand up rather than sit down. After a year or so, it wouldn't ever occur to me to sit down. I would stand on a completely empty bus. I was doing that once and this nice old man got on, watched me for a couple of stops, then motioned to offer me a seat on the empty row across from him. I thought murderous thoughts towards him and walked to stand at the back of the bus where I could be free from his infuriating kindness.

There were countless learned and automatic actions when it came to food and movement. The way I prepared what I ate, the way I cleaned the kitchen in the same order before, during, and after eating. All the movement compulsions from exercise to walking to standing up when I could have been sitting. They all became automatic. I didn't have to think to do them. In recovery, however, I did have to become very mindful and conscious of my actions in order to stop doing them.

LEARNED THOUGHTS

As my entrenched behaviours developed, so did thought patterns that went alongside them. I think initially our brains use thoughts to help us justify what we are doing. At least, mine would. Say, for example, I had been offered a sandwich and I had felt that little freak-out and declined it, my brain would think something like *"bread isn't good for me"* to help me try and make sense of my own reaction. After a while, those thoughts became a go-to, and would be there as soon as I saw, thought about or was offered something like a sandwich.

Calorie counting became automatic, and the thought that went alongside the counting was usually the *"calories in equals calories out"* saying that I once heard a personal trainer in the gym utter. (It's not true, by the way — our bodies are far more complicated than that.) *"Calories in equals calories out"* would play itself in the back of my mind like a wasp buzzing around my head.

Hard-wired thoughts like these can be insanely distracting. Depressingly so. It used to upset me the amount of time my brain would default to these annoying and boring thought patterns. I'm so happy to say that recovery brings a much clearer, and less prone to auto-play, brain.

So, take all these things together and you can see that we don't just have to rewire actions in recovery, we must rewire words, emotional reactions, thoughts and — here's a big one — belief systems.

LEARNED BELIEF SYSTEMS

Everything you believe in is learned. I hate to break that to you. I also hate to think of myself as that … influenced by the environment. Even your genetics can't fully determine your belief systems (although I do believe they influence them). Don't worry, Buttercup, I'm not saying you are not unique. You are. I'm just saying you are — we all are — products of our environment in some way or another. We are being socially conditioned from the moment the umbilical cord is cut.

Nobody came out of the womb believing in Baby Jesus. Nobody was born knowing that the world is round. And nobody came into this world believing that their body must be thin to be acceptable.

I like this quote from Peter Halligan, a psychologist at Cardiff University: *"Belief has been a most powerful component of human nature that has somewhat been neglected. But it has been capitalised on by marketing agents, politics and religion for the best part of two millennia."*

Our brains like to form belief systems because they are helpful in streamlining our decision-making process and aid the automation of that process. If you believe in God, then that belief means that you don't have to spend a lot of time deciding whether or not you believe in God every time you listen to a sermon in church. Instead, you have a base for everything else you learn to sit on and grow off. It's far more efficient.

Of course, our experiences shape our belief systems in a way that is probably designed to keep us safe. If you have been bitten by the only dog that you have ever met, you may shape the belief that all dogs bite. So then you start to act as if all dogs bite by being nervous around dogs ... then they bite you because you being nervous makes them nervous.

I must admit I find belief systems fascinating (well, social neuroscience in general). How something can be so useful and so destructive at the same time. How once a person believes something, it is so incredibly hard to shake that belief, regardless of the information, evidence, and science they are given to oppose it. As an atheist, observing religious beliefs in others intrigues me, and helps me understand the strength of learned belief systems.

I have seen that our belief systems can be biologically influenced by changes in our biological experience. My grandmother, a long time devout Christian, suffered a stroke. When she recovered, she was no longer a devout Christian. He faith gone. As if the stroke had amputated that part of her brain. Some people have this work the other way; they experience illness and it influences them to seek religious faith. I felt a belief system change as I developed anorexia. Of course, I didn't know what was happening at the time. I thought I was seeing the light — or my version of it. I thought for all these years I had been wrong, I had been eating wrong and living wrong. Restriction felt so bloody great, and it all made sense in my head. It all lined up. I was changing, but I was convinced it was for the better. I very much feel that anorexia sparked the belief that to be a good person, I had to eat as little as possible and move as much as possible. That makes sense if you are looking at anorexia through a biological lens, as a migration response to perceived scarce resources. That belief took a while to grow. It wasn't as strong in the first year, but my behaviours continuing to inform my brain that it must be true made it incredibly strong by the second year. To the point where the "old me," the person who ate what she wanted and sat on the couch, felt like another life away.

In fact, this is yet another plug for the necessity of early intervention — we need to stop people going down the eating disorder rabbit hole before their belief systems get too heavily corrupted.

So, what forms our beliefs?

- Everything you pay attention to
- Everything you watch
- Everything you read
- Everything you think about
- Conversations you have
- Conversations you listen to
- Podcasts you listen to
- Celebrities you admire
- Politicians
- What you were taught in school
- Your family's beliefs
- Your friends' beliefs
- Your wider culture's beliefs

There are more things I could add to that list. You get the gist. Your brain is always watching, always learning, always absorbing. Your brain is learning from what you do, and from what others do. We are all influenced by one another, often more than we like to think.

The troubling thing about a belief system is that, once it is formed, our brains have this knack of translating the world to fit into what we believe. Founder of "*Skeptic*" magazine, Michael Shermer, attributes much of this to the brain's readiness to perceive patterns and to then attribute agency. Once a belief has been constructed, our brains will protect it by rationalising in a way to support that belief regardless of what happens. Humans will protect their beliefs even when the cost of doing so is very high. We have plenty of history books to show us that strongly held beliefs can be destructive.

Environment aside, I think that when I developed anorexia, even if I were in a social vacuum, I would have still developed the belief that eating more food than I perceived to be the minimal amount I needed was an awful thing to do. Sure, society heaped on top of this with all its "nutritional science," and lead to the fully formed, polished and dusted belief that I ended up with about fat being the devil. But the seed, the distrust of food, especially highly nutrient dense food, came part and parcel of my neat little anorexia genetic package. And once that was there, my brain had plenty of "information" to pluck out of the world and plug into that belief package to support and strengthen it.

I did manage to rewire my belief that I had to eat as little as possible and move as much as possible, eventually. But would I have been able to do that without nutritionally rehabilitating somewhat first? Without those anorexia genetics firing less, as they tend to do when we nutritionally rehabilitate some? I doubt it. The point is, I don't believe that there is much point in trying to neurally rewire unless you are also nutritionally rehabilitated, or getting yourself there.

CHANGING BELIEFS
FOR RECOVERY

The good news is (and I can't believe I am writing this) that brainwashing works. If you take a radical and lock them away from their cultural influences and pelt them with your own beliefs for long enough, it may take many years, but eventually you will change their beliefs and replace them with your own (I say that like I have done it; I haven't, but the concept is interesting).

In recovery, I brainwashed myself with messages that opposed those of my eating disorder. I have witnessed hundreds of other people do the same in their own recoveries. They surround themselves with recovery messages, stop following all the diet and fitness accounts on Instagram, and brainwash themselves with the words they know they need to hear. Usually along the lines of *"eat the fucking food."* We can manually change our belief systems if we give it a good enough crack, and this is exactly what we need to do in recovery.

WHERE DOES YOUR
BRAIN GET ITS DATA?

Okay, so we have established that your brain is basically an ever watching, neural-pathway-forming, data-gathering version of big brother. Where is it getting this data from? The answer is, everything. Everything you think, and everything you do.

HOW EVERYTHING YOU DO INFORMS YOUR BRAIN

Action requires moving muscles and therefore action requires energy. Energy is a resource. I find it easier to understand that by thinking of energy as money. Anything that means you have to spend money usually causes you to pay attention, because money is important to you. Well, energy is important to your body. Anything that causes you to act, your brain is going to pay particular attention to. If you act, your brain will conclude that whatever prompted you to act must be important. Actions can be small, but they will still inform your brain.

For example. You are standing in a shop trying to choose a sandwich to eat. You see the calorie information and you change your action as a result. You pick up the lower calorie sandwich. Your brain learned from that, that calories must contain important information. Otherwise, why would you have altered your choice? Why would you have changed your behaviour? Why would you have taken different action? You wouldn't have. But you did. Therefore, calories are important. Unimportant information would not have caused you to change your action.

Now think about all the times you have acted as if calories are important. This is the reason your brain pays so much attention to calories, because your actions over the years have taught your brain that it should.

It may be true that, initially, anorexia drove your desire to steer away from more caloric foods. But after a while that doesn't matter. Once something has become neurally wired, the original "reason" is no longer required for you to continue to take that action. So even if you nutritionally rehabilitated to the point your anorexia genetic response to energy deficit was shut off, the wiring that anorexia created while it was active will remain — unless, of course, you rewire.

It's like the military veteran who still lines up their wardrobe the night before as if they have inspection the next day. They may have been honourably discharged 10 years ago, and the need for their meticulous readiness long gone, but the behaviour got wired in, hence they do it by rote.

HOW WHAT YOU PAY MENTAL ATTENTION TO INFLUENCES YOUR BRAIN

"Where your attention goes, energy flows."

If you pay mental attention to something, by doing so you teach your brain that thing is important. Why would you have paid it attention if it were not?

Back to the calorie example. Think of all the times you have looked up calorie information. Think of all the times you have turned over a food package to look at the nutrition information. Think of all the times you have sat there and counted calories in your head. Is it any wonder that your brain is obsessed with calories? By paying attention to calories, you have taught your brain that calories are important.

What about weight? Think of all the times you have paid attention to weight in some way or another. Paying attention to the number on the scale. Looking up those stupid BMI charts. No wonder your brain is obsessed with weight numbers, right?

Now, what about wallpaper? What about wall paint? Can you look at the colour of the paint on any wall in your house, or your friend's house, and tell me what the colour code is? What about the wall that is closest to you right now? Can you tell me the hex code of the colour on it? You probably can't — unless you are a painter or an interior designer. If you are a painter, you would have paid a lot of mental attention to wall colour codes, so you likely know many of those off by heart. Your brain has learned that wall colours are important, hence you retain information like that. If you walk into a house, the paint job is probably the first thing you see.

But unless you are a wall painter or interior designer by trade, I bet you would struggle to even remember the colour of the walls in your best friend's kitchen. I am sure you can remember what sort of milk they buy though, can't you? Because you pay close attention to food.

What we pay attention to determines what we pay attention to!

It is true that your anorexia is what instigated your obsession with things like food, calories, weight, etc. But over the years, these have become neurally entrenched. So it is likely that by now, even if you nutritionally rehabilitate, unless you also neurally rewire, you will continue to be obsessed with these things.

PRACTICAL APPLICATION?

I know that many researchers, scientists, behaviourists, therapists and psychologists understand the theory of what neural rewiring is. I believe that people with lived experience can help immensely to add texture to theory, and we are a critical part of truly understanding how theory works in real life.

Here is an example. It may seem like a good idea, when trying to help someone rewire an exercise compulsion, to tell them to do some other "less harmful" type of movement. Instead of their usual run, for example, it may be suggested that they go for a walk, or take a yoga class. And every time I hear this, I scream "NO, NO, NO!" inside. Because you can't truly rewire movement compulsion with movement. I have no published neuroscientific theory to support this (yet! Maybe one day.), I just know it was the hard truth for me, and for many people I have worked with. Oh, believe me, I tried for years to "do less" movement. Failed. The hardest and scariest thing I have ever done in my life was go cold turkey on exercise, and doing so was critical for my path to full recovery. Movement is movement. Lower-level movement is still lighting up that movement pathway in the brain. Running compulsions will be replaced with walking compulsions. HIIT classes will be replaced with cleaning-the-house movement. A brain with a compulsion to move will take any movement it can get and hold onto it in a way that somebody without lived experience can't possibly comprehend. It's like taking a roulette gambler and telling them to take a break by going for a day out to the racetrack.

These neural associations are so much more complicated and far-reaching than something as simple as: *"Running is an eating disorder behaviour but walking is not."*

We must rewire all sorts of associations to recover fully. In the movement category alone, there may be hundreds of beliefs that need rewiring. Such as:

- I need to move more than the other people in my family to eat the same amount as them
- I need to move after eating
- I need to move before eating
- I need to stand on the bus to be able to eat lunch
- I need to walk to the coffee machine at work if anyone else gets up and walks over there

Those are just a few. Are any of those actions going to kill someone? No. Are any of them even going to lead to weight loss? Unlikely. Are any of them going to stop someone fully recovering? Absolutely.

So you can see that, when it is suggested that a person replace working out in the gym with walking instead, or another movement, we are trying to shoot a tiger with a spud gun. Many entrenched thoughts and behaviours are like the hairline roots that sprout off the main roots of the tree. Some of them are so small that nobody else would be able to detect them. And this is the very reason I am always saying that the only person who can get you recovered is you! You are the only person who can know that some of these compulsive thoughts or behaviours are even alive. Hence, for treatment providers who can't possibly know the almost invisible hairline roots that are growing off the main roots in a person's behaviours, the only safe course of action is to say, *"Move as little as possible,"* and, *"No exercise."* Kill the tiger with a bazooka!

Nobody wants to tell a person with an eating disorder and compulsive movement to completely stop. That usually provokes tears and tantrums and negotiations. But this heightened emotional state at even the suggestion of stopping movement is exactly why it is so important. We need to show our brains that we can eat and we don't have to move to justify eating. We must rewire that very notion, and replacing movement with movement doesn't counter the belief that we need to move in order to eat.

To truly rewire my movement compulsion, I had to redirect to an activity that involved being still. It was hard for me to do, it is hard for others to do. But I see people with eating disorders do this daily, so let's not underestimate them.

REDIRECTS

A redirect is an alternative action, thought, behaviour. Often, the best redirects are the opposite action from the one you are trying to rewire. Instead, let's take the action of eating *more* food when restriction feels like the hard-wired default. In rewiring movement compulsions, stillness can be a redirect. Compulsive movement usually requires a redirect that involves sitting — and there are plenty of activity options that we can sit and do. When I was in recovery, I used sitting and writing as a go-to redirect for my compulsion to stand and/or move constantly.

Not all redirects are equal

In the example of compulsive exercise, many of us also have to rewire our tendency to choose any activity that involves more movement over something that involves stillness. So yes, even the decision-making process of what we choose to do instead of our compulsive behaviours is often something we must rewire!

For example, had you given me three options of redirects when I felt the urge to go to the gym, and those three things were: 1) go for a short and slow walk; 2) watch TV; or 3) play Scrabble, without even thinking about it I would have chosen #1. I would always choose movement, no matter how slow, no matter how small. I had to work hard to rewire this default. I had to force myself to always choose something that involved sitting. Eventually, with full recovery, and because I consistently rewired my compulsion to choose movement, I would find myself in a place of being able to freely choose activities because I enjoyed them — movement or not.

The best, most effective redirect is always the one that feels the hardest.

STAGES OF IDENTIFICATION AND REWIRING

In order to rewire anything at all, you need to be able to identify it. Often, thoughts aren't that obvious to us; they are more like feelings or inclinations. If you can't identify a thought pattern or behaviour, good luck changing it. So, identification or detection has to be the first goal when we are rewiring. There are two levels of rewiring identification as I see it:

1 - The Fucking Obvious Stuff – purging, heavy restriction, excessive exercise, etc.
2 - The Subtle But Pernicious Stuff – inclinations, back-of-the-mind rules, tendencies.

"The Fucking Obvious Stuff" is … fucking obvious. It is blatantly destructive in many cases, and a "typical" eating disorder thought, behaviour or reaction. Generally, it is something that clearly has the intention of bodyweight suppression behind it. With purging, for example, it is hard to argue that self-induced vomiting is good for you. With compulsive exercise, it is very plain that this behaviour is there to suppress bodyweight and is excessive. Without outright restriction, it is quite easy to see that not enough food is being eaten. These are the fucking obvious things that need redirecting, and most people in recovery can identify these.

"The Subtle But Pernicious Stuff" is harder to see. It is your tendency to walk the longer route than really needed, or to always happen to choose an activity that involves movement over one that requires more stillness. It is your inclination towards "healthy" food choices. It is that feeling of irritability you get if you are in a situation where you can't completely control your food choices or serving sizes. It is the rules that play silently in the back of your mind that you can pretend are not there, but that do influence the way that you go about your day.

Many people get through to stage one rewiring in recovery. They are able to identify and stop the fucking obvious stuff. These are also the things that most treatment providers can recognise. If you can stop the fucking obvious stuff, your life and your health will be better. Granted.

"Better" is not fully recovered. Sadly, I think most people in recovery from an eating disorder recover only to the stage of "better" from the fucking obvious stuff. They never make it onto level two, which is identifying and rewiring the subtle stuff. Therefore, they never make it to the freedom that is being fully recovered.

I want you to make it to full recovery. Nothing less. So, we have to focus on the subtle stuff too. And when I say "we," I mean "you." Because nobody else can fully identify all the subtle stuff for you — although close family members are often very insightful about these and can help you identify the ones you don't really want to admit to or see. I can give you plenty of examples and help you see it, but ultimately, we are all unique enough in our weird shit that you will be the one to truly nail this down.

Here are some examples from a session with a client of mine when we were differentiating between, and listing some level one and level two identification of, rewiring targets:

Fucking Obvious Stuff

- Not eating enough at breakfast and lunch — blatant restriction.

- Continuing to compulsively move or exercise.
- Chewing and spitting.

Subtle Stuff

- Using the need to save money as an excuse not to adequately shop for food.
- Waiting until the next meal or snack time to eat rather than eating as soon as hungry.
- Being "too busy" to prepare and eat what I really want, so falling back to eating the same "safe" foods all the time.
- Walking/standing when I really want to sit.
- Engaging in the feeling of guilt after I have eaten more than I usually do.
- Engaging in negative thoughts about weight gain.
- Sneaking a look at calorie information on packets.
- Engaging in the compulsion to look at other people's bodies and try and work out how much they weigh.
- Having to eat slightly less than everyone else at the table.
- Body checking and weighing myself.
- At work, suggesting that my colleague and I take a "walk around the block" whenever we need to have a one to one meeting rather than finding an empty conference room to talk in.

One of the things that makes the subtle behaviours so pernicious is that these are often behaviours that are, arguably, not disordered in plain sight. When seen in a person without an eating disorder, they may be normal. Take the last one in that list, the walk around the block with the colleague at work. If a person doesn't have a history of compulsive movement, this is not a disordered behaviour at all. Take the example of feeling slightly hungry but deciding to wait until the next meal to eat, rather than eat as soon as possible. This sort of thing is pretty "normal" for a lot of people. It is likely not harmful to them either. But the very same behaviour can be something that keeps a person in recovery from a restrictive eating disorder from fully recovering. And this is one of the things that makes identifying and rewiring the subtle stuff so difficult: your brain can easily persuade you that there is nothing wrong with the behaviour, that it is "normal", that your friends do it, that it is nothing to bother yourself with.

It is. And you *must* "bother yourself" with it.

Taken alone, none of these subtle behaviours seem altogether that much of a big deal. Most of them won't even have much of an impact on your physical health. But collectively, they add up to a neural cage surrounding you that interferes with your ability to be completely free and happy. This happens so often when a person nutritionally rehabilitates, stops the fucking obvious behaviours, but doesn't neurally rewire the subtle stuff. It is a lonely and confusing place to be, because on physical measures you are told that you should be fully recovered, yet you know that you are not but can't work out why. Nor can anyone else. So you give up on yourself and assume that you are broken. You're not. Your brain is doing exactly what it has been taught to do — you just need to identify the subtle barriers and rewire yourself out of them.

Not sure what's an eating disorder pathway and what isn't? Blow them all up!

If you have had an eating disorder for a long time, it is often so entwined into your life that it is hard to tell what is an eating disorder neural pathway and what isn't. And to be honest, neural pathways aren't quite that straightforward anyway. It's not like there are these neat lines in your brain labelled "Eating Disorder Neural Pathway Only." The eating disorder behaviors are associated with day-to-day actions and behaviours too because you have been acting them out in parallel with your other more domestic activities. Eating disorder neural pathways and your day-to-day life are all intertwined.

Never fear, the bazooka approach works. It is often the easiest way to ensure you are disentangling yourself from the neural pathways associated with your eating disorder. If in doubt, blow your whole routine out the sky.

Say, for example, your morning routine. Wake up, get up, go to the loo, brush teeth, wash face, get dressed, make bed, go downstairs, empty the dishwasher, do your complusive exercise routine, prepare breakfast, tidy the kitchen, eat breakfast ... You can tell that the complusive exercise part is your eating disorder and you know you need to change what you have for breakfast but what about all the stuff before that? Do you do things in that same order because it is most convenient, or somehow is the order in which you do all those things tied in to what feels safe? Are things like tidying the kitchen and emptying the dishwasher there to push back eating breakfast? What about making the bed? Is that just another busy complusive movement task that you don't really need to do?

When you don't really know, the best approach is to change everything. If you feel resistance to changing it then you know it was certainly something that you were attached to and needed to change. If you don't feel any resistance, then you didn't lose anything by changing your routine anyway. While bazooka-ing your whole daily routine may seem drastic, it is a guaranteed way to scrape that whole neural network and start building a new one that isn't contaminated with eating disorders associations.

SUPER-HIGHWAYS

In working with hundreds of other people on rewiring from eating disorders, I have noticed some themes to do with the things we have to rewire. One of these I call "super-highways."

Super-highways are behaviours, or groups of behaviours, that seem to be at the core of our eating disorder neural networks. When we light them up, they supply that network with a lot of strength, or energy. Just like a highway provides a lot of traffic into a town, these neural highways are like injections of energy for our eating disorder when we activate them.

The two most common super-highways that feed energy to an eating disorder mind-set, in my experience, are compulsive movement and "healthy" eating. Those of us with a compulsive movement element to our eating disorder tend to find that this is one of the strongest and hardest compulsions to break. The same is true for that tendency to eat in a "healthy" manner — aka orthorexia.

For most people in recovery, compulsive movement and orthorexic eating will be the things that take the longest to rewire. They will also usually be the tendencies that trip you up months after you think that you are over the hardest stages of recovery.

Here's one example. A client has overcome compulsive exercise very well and not been to the gym in four months. She feels that she is over the compulsive movement stuff, and her GP has commented that she should start doing some exercise again. So she joins a gym with the idea of only participating in a couple of weights classes a week. A month later, she has noticed that she is struggling with increased feelings of guilt after eating, and having anxiety again at the thought of spontaneously eating out with friends. Is it a coincidence that these thoughts and feelings have made a subtle comeback at this time? Or is it linked to the increase in exercise?

Another example: Bob has been in recovery for three months from restriction and purging. He embraced unrestricted eating and the required rewiring efforts, and has been doing very well. He feels much more freedom in his choices, and his mental hunger has diminished. He visits his dentist for a routine clean, and the hygienist mentions that sugar causes tooth decay. Bob decides to try and eat a little "healthier" by reducing the amount of sugar in his diet. A couple of weeks later, he complains to me that his tendency to eat the same foods for lunch each day has increased again, and he had begun to battle with thoughts around purging. Is it a coincidence that these thoughts and feelings have made a subtle comeback at this time? Or is it linked to the "healthy eating" sugar reduction (restriction)?

If I had only seen this sort of thing happen once or twice, I might say it was a coincidence. But I've seen it happen time and time again. It is, luckily, pretty easy to pull someone out of, as they can usually see the turn of events and link the increase in eating disorder tendencies back to the change in their action. Time and time again, the super-highways that lead to increased traffic to other eating disorder neural pathways are compulsive movement and "healthy" eating (orthorexic tendencies). It is worth paying special attention to these two things, even when you feel that you are in a much better place in recovery mentally.

REWIRING EXAMPLES

As I said, this book has to be short! So, let's get straight into some of the common aspects of rewiring.

REWIRING YOUR FEAR OF NOT SUPPRESSING YOUR BODYWEIGHT (FEAR OF WEIGHT GAIN)

Many of us who develop eating disorders also develop the belief that our bodies are not acceptable unless we are suppressing them. As I explain in detail in *RRR!*, you do not have to be extremely underweight to be at a suppressed bodyweight.

Even those of us who didn't have body image problems before we had an eating disorder act as if we are afraid to gain weight when we have an active eating disorder. I believe the majority of this is a biological influence sparked by the eating disorder genetics, but that some of it is learned from our culture too. If you have the genetics for an eating disorder, when you go into energy deficit and the eating disorder develops, I believe that part of that genetic package is a fear of eating more than the minimum amount you need to survive.

If the genetic package sparked by energy deficit unleashed the fear of weight gain, you might think that amending energy deficit would be enough to resolve that fear. In cases when a person has only had an eating disorder a short period of time, it often is. But, for those with long-term eating disorders, every day that we act as if we are scared of weight gain, our brain learns to be scared of weight gain. Neural wiring has been taking place, and this doesn't just go away on its own when we amend energy deficit.

For many of us with an eating disorder, it's our own actions that teach our brains to believe that weight gain is a bad thing. For example, you see the calories on a packet of cookies and then decide not to eat them, instead choosing a lower calorie granola bar. What information does your ever-watchful brain take away from that episode? Your brain will conclude, from your actions, that weight gain must be a bad thing. When you avoid calories, you are *acting* as if weight gain is a bad thing. How can you expect your brain to be okay with the concept of you gaining weight if you are still acting as if it is something to be avoided? Your action — the action of eating the lower calorie granola bar instead — informed your brain that it must be true that weight gain must be avoided.

It is important to understand that even if you have gained weight in recovery, you can still be *acting* as if you want to suppress your bodyweight by your choices. You can also still be engaging in thought patterns that are negative about your bodyweight and your weight gain. In doing so, you will cause your brain to conclude that your body is a problem. Many people get frustrated in this stage of recovery as they have gained some weight but still have a huge mental issue with their body, and have a large fear of further weight gain. This is because you can gain weight and still be acting as if weight gain is bad as you do so; if you act and think as if weight gain is bad, your brain will not change its belief that you must be at a suppressed bodyweight to be acceptable. Countless times I have spoken to people in this stage of recovery who are frustrated because they have gained weight but not noticing mental state changes. Then I point out they are still drinking diet coke. Diet coke is designed for people actively suppressing their bodies. How the heck can you expect your brain to believe that your unsuppressed bodyweight is okay when you still choose to drink a product designed for people who are on diets? That's like telling someone you love them while slapping them in the face. Your actions are not supporting your intentions.

If you want your brain to believe that you don't have to be on a diet, you have to stop acting like you are on a diet.

Act like you mean it!

As a recovery coach, I often work with people who want to fully recover but still *act* as if their unsuppressed bodyweight is a bad thing. We cannot expect our beliefs to change if we are still acting as if they are true. Your actions inform your brain, remember, so you must act the way that you want your brain to think. If you want your brain to be okay with your unsuppressed bodyweight, you absolutely must stop acting as if your unsuppressed body-weight is something to be avoided.

Now think of all the thousands of actions you have taken this past couple of months that would give your brain the impression that your unsuppressed bodyweight is a bad thing. Here are a few you might have done:

- Not eating when hungry: Why would you not eat when hungry if weight gain were not a bad thing?
- Choosing a lower calorie food: Why would you choose the lower calorie option if weight gain was okay?
- Purging: Why would you purge your food for any other reason than not wanting to gain weight?
- Compulsive movement: Why would you compulsively move if it were okay to gain weight?
- Body checking: If weight gain were okay, why would you need to body check?
- Chewing and spitting: Why would you spit food out and not just eat it unless you didn't want to gain weight?
- Engaging in negative body image thoughts: Why would

you give these thoughts so much mental attention if they weren't important?

- Drinking diet drinks: Don't even get me started.

And here's the important thing to understand about neural rewiring and recovery. You can have all the good intentions to recover in the world, but if you are still acting as if you are avoiding your natural unsuppressed bodyweight, your brain is still being taught, via your actions, that your body is a bad thing.

The actions must come first, because your actions inform your brain.

You must start acting as if you are not afraid of weight gain if you don't want to be afraid of weight gain.

You must stop acting as if you are on a diet if you don't want to live like you are on a diet.

You must start acting as if you like your unsuppressed body if you want to like your unsuppressed body.

You won't change your brain's beliefs first. It doesn't work that way. You have to change your actions first. Your actions have taught your brain that weight gain is bad, and your actions will have to un-teach that. And your brain will scream about it during the initial learning process, but if you are consistent, your belief system will change.

REWIRING NEGATIVE BODY IMAGE

Negative thoughts or feelings towards one's own body are also learned. For some of us, they are learned before we develop an eating disorder, and can be a contributing factor to energy deficit. For others, they are part and parcel of the eating disorder package and only develop after onset. Whichever way negative body image neural pathways came about, we rewire them the same way: by stopping engaging with them.

Remember that your brain is watching which thoughts you pay mental attention to. It is learning that the thoughts and feelings you pay mental attention to must be important. This means every time you engage in a negative thought pattern about your body, your brain is learning to think negatively about your body. It is a truly vicious cycle and one you can feel that there is no way out of. But there is! You just have to be very conscious of your thoughts, and intentional about your redirects. Like any other skill, rewiring takes time, patience and a lot of practice. If your true intention is to learn how to move through and direct your own thoughts, you will work out how to achieve that. The brain is like a muscle in that the more you focus on learning how to use it, the more skilled you will become at using it.

Unlike actions, thoughts are not quite as obvious to detect and redirect. Rewiring is something that we all learn to do by having the intention of doing it. It is almost impossible to write someone a step-by-step guide on how to ignore or move through a thought. It is rather like trying to write a manual on how to flex your arm, or trying to teach a child how to walk. There are exercises and guides, but it is just one of those things you must want to do, be determined to do, and work out for yourself.

That said, I wrote a whole toolkit of mind exercises in *RRR!* To practice thought ignoring, the *"Back to Black"* technique is the one I tell people to get good at first. That is a meditation that helps with the ability to "drop" and move past a thought once it has already started.

When you are feeling frustrated because you are having trouble ignoring thoughts, the biggest piece of advice I can give you is to remember that you learned to walk once. You worked that out through sheer determination, and you will work this out too. You just have to keep getting up.

REWIRING NEGATIVE BODY IMAGE ACTIONS

There are plenty of actions that contribute to negative body image. Actions are easier to identify and rewire than thoughts, and the obvious actions that contribute to negative body image are those designed to suppress your natural body weight. Anything in the "fucking obvious stuff" category — such as restriction, purging and compulsive movement — also teaches your brain not to like the idea of your unsuppressed body. In addition, there are plenty of subtle actions. Here are a few common ones:

- Body checking: Whenever you body check, you give your brain the message that you must stay at a suppressed bodyweight. Therefore, you contribute to negative body image ideas about your unsuppressed bodyweight.
- Weighing yourself: The only real reason you weigh yourself is because you are scared of gaining "too much" weight.
- Comparing your body to other people's bodies: Spending mental energy on body comparisons gives your brain the impression that body comparisons are needed and important.
- Drinking diet drinks: I know I keep harping on about diet drinks, but that's because they are such a culturally accepted way of feeding the belief system that thin is good and fat is bad. Your brain is always watching and learning, and your choices are always sending a message.

The problem that many people in recovery face, as outlined in the previous chapter, is that we expect our negative body image stuff to miraculously go away even though we are still participating in thoughts, reactions, and actions that contribute to it. Negative body image can't amend itself if you are actively reinforcing it via your thoughts and actions multiple times a day. If you want your negative body image belief to change, your actions and your thoughts must change first. You must teach your brain that there is nothing wrong with your body, and you do this by acting as if there is nothing wrong with your body. Stop acting as if you are on a diet — start by putting down the diet coke and avoiding anything with the label "low-" on it: low-fat, low-carb, low-sugar ... it all leads to negative body image.

REWIRING NEGATIVE BODY IMAGE EMOTIONAL REACTIONS

With the body image aspects of rewiring, we should focus on reactions too. For example, you catch a glimpse of your image in a shop mirror. Your reaction to realising that your reflection is there may be to linger on it, and to analyse it. If you engage in this reaction, you just taught your brain that your reflection is important, and the critical thoughts that you listened to confirmed that there is something wrong with you.

When you have a negative body image, your brain is already hyper-aware of your body. We don't need to encourage that. We need to discourage it. So we have to interrupt the reaction that is the desire to stop and look and be critical. We must walk on by regardless of how tempting it feels to stop.

Another example may be the reaction that you experience when feeling the flesh around your stomach. Your brain has been wired to associate the feeling of this flesh with negative emotions, such as shame and disgust. Because you previously engaged in these negative emotions when becoming aware of flesh on your body, your brain has learned that the feeling of shame and disgust must be relevant and appropriate in this sort of circumstance. They are not, and you must teach your brain that the emotions of shame and disgust are not appropriate by ignoring them and moving on.

It is always a choice to engage with an emotion. It may not feel like a choice, because emotions are designed to be convincing, but it is. You will recognise these common neurally wired emotional reactions to your body and be able to work out how to intercept them. How to say "no" to them. How to not get pulled in to the story of the emotion. You should prepare yourself for them. It's not like any of them should take you by surprise. Most of them probably happen multiple times a day. Here are some common examples of body image reactions to rewire:

- Feeling your thighs touch one another is often wired to the emotion of disgust.
- Feeling your stomach is full after a meal is often wired to the emotion of guilt.
- Feeling your waistbands tighter around your waist is often wired to the feeling of panic.
- Feeling your own flesh as you get dressed or undressed is often wired to the emotion of shame.
- Feeling the flesh on your stomach is often wired to the emotion of repulsion.

These are common examples; you can probably add some of your own. Start to challenge yourself to intercept the feeling of your body from the negative emotion that is associated with it. Of course, the big one here is the negative emotional reaction you might have about weight gain. You must learn how to move over those associations and reactions, and not allow yourself to engage with negative emotions about weight gain.

Not engaging in emotional reactions sounds, and often feels, like it is impossible, but you do it all the time. We all do. Well, at least, most of us do. I did it yesterday when I didn't engage in the desire to sit on the floor of Costco and cry like a baby because they were out of cheesecake. I also did it last week when I didn't scream at the flight staff who told us we would be stuck on the runway for two hours before take-off—instead, I made the decision to ignore my feelings of rage and enjoy watching a movie. I have to choose to move past my own emotional reactions a lot when working with horses, in fact, I did it this morning when I was working with a young mustang—I had to shed the frustration I was feeling because I knew him sensing that from me would not work in my favour.

You do have the skill of not engaging in emotional reactions. You just need to develop it to the level of a super-skill for the purposes of recovery.

REWIRING THE FEELINGS OF WRONGDOING AFTER EATING DIFFERENTLY

The feeling of "wrongdoing" after eating more than usual, or differently than usual, is very common among people with eating disorders. It is another example of an emotional reaction that your brain has learned to associate with an action or situation. I do think that there is a biological initiation for this feeling of wrongdoing after eating more than you think that you "need" with the onset of anorexia that stems from the migration genetic package. It isn't just a coincidence that all people with anorexia feel this guilt if we eat more than what we perceive to be "needed," it has to be biologically wired for a purpose. If you are supposed to be migrating it serves you best to eat only the minimal amount that you need and then get up and keep migrating. The brain is using the emotions of guilt and shame to motivate you to not stop around all day long and get going!

Regardless of where this emotion stemmed from originally, you still need to rewire it. Because you *engaged* in the feeling of wrongdoing every time you ate more or differently, your brain has learned over time that this feeling must be the appropriate emotional reaction to accompany the event of eating more than usual. It isn't, so we must teach your brain that this emotional reaction is no longer relevant. And — you guessed it — we do that by refusing to engage with the emotional feeling of wrongdoing. Save that feeling for the next time you rob a bank, murder someone, or actually do something wrong!

When it came to rewiring this feeling, I found it personally helpful to see this sort of reaction as a vice that I had to stop indulging in. Reframing it in this way is what allowed me to see that there was nothing honourable or noble in continuing to engage in the story that I was a bad person because I was eating what my body needed. As I mention in *RRR!* there is a real martyr effect that eating disorders tend to have on us. In some twisted sense, engaging in feelings of wrongdoing after eating used to make me feel virtuous. When I could see that dynamic, I considered it pretty self-indulgent to allow myself to engage in feelings that should only be engaged in if I had truly done something bloody awful. Then I could turn it around in my head that engaging in feelings of wrongdoing was a bad habit I had to pull myself out of.

That was my own mental process around feelings of wrongdoing and eating. At least, that is as close as I can put it into words. You will develop your own — you just need the intention to do so.

REWIRING FEAR OF UNRESTRICTED EATING (BODY TRUST AND COMMUNICATION)

It took me a heck of a long time to identify that the resistance I felt towards certain foods was actually fear. Fear can be weird like that. My logical brain thought it preposterous that I would be scared of food, so it didn't want to consider that could be the case. My reptile brain, however, was certainly afraid of eating anything other than small portions of highly caloric or fatty foods. That, I consider, is part of the genetic package of an eating disorder. Initially.

Over the years of avoiding certain types of food, and acting as if I was afraid of certain types of food, that fear response to eating certain foods in an unrestricted manner became hard-wired. The original reason for it was irrelevant; my brain was going to fire off a fear response at the thought of eating those foods because I had trained it to do so.

Again, when we fall into the problem of a hard-wired reaction, nutritional rehabilitation alone usually won't amend it. We must neurally rewire too. That means teaching your brain that there are no foods to be afraid of. And how do we do this? We eat the fucking foods. In unrestricted quantities.

This means eating to physical and mental hunger. One of the conflicting aspects of eating disorders is that you can simultaneously desire to eat a certain food in large quantities and be afraid of doing so. Remember that thinking about eating is mental hunger, and in recovery most of us obsess about the very foods we are most scared of. That's because your brain knows it needs nutrient dense foods. Feast follows famine. Eating a lot of food after restricting is, I think, a biological necessity. Our ancestors wouldn't have sat around writing up meal plans after a famine, they would have got busy doing a lot of glorious, messy, eating.

The fabulous thing about unrestricted eating is that it allows you to achieve both nutritional rehabilitation and neural rewiring. It is your golden ticket to full recovery. I can't stress how important it is — well actually, I can, and I did so in *RRR*!

Let's look more into the rewiring of that fear of certain foods, or certain quantities of certain foods.

Take, for example, a double cheeseburger, fries and a milkshake. After years of avoiding this sort of meal, my brain had learnt that this sort of meal should be avoided. I taught my brain that, by the action of avoidance. In fact, I had taught my brain that any component of this sort of meal should be avoided (despite the fact I obsessed about it all the time). So it is no shock that eating this sort of meal in recovery is met with anxiety, is it?

As I have mentioned, the hard part for me was recognising fear. Fear didn't present itself as fear in the traditional sense. It presented itself as excuses. I had all these excuses. Most of them, ironically, were linked to "health." *Everyone knows it isn't healthy to eat too much fat blah blah blah.*

OMFG. That "health" excuse. If I had really been looking out for my "health" I would have logically seen that blatantly ignoring what my body was asking me for is the least "healthy" action. Yet this "health" excuse very conveniently allowed me to hide behind it. It masked my truth, being that I was plain old scared of eating that much. I feared gaining weight if I did. Pretty standard eating disorder fears hiding behind a culturally acceptable excuse not to eat. (Again.)

In this example, we have more than one thing to rewire. Here is what we have:

- I have to rewire my fear of cheeseburgers, fries and milkshakes by eating cheeseburgers, fries and milkshakes until my brain has learned the avoidance reaction must no longer be appropriate. I do this by eating the food as frequently as I like, without restriction.
- I have to rewire that "health" excuse by not engaging in that story when it comes up as a reason not to eat. By, in fact, doing the opposite of what that story wants, by eating the food.
- I have to rewire my distrust of the communication that my body is giving to me via my physical and/or mental hunger. I do this by eating the food.
- I have to rewire my fear of eating large quantities of nutrient-dense foods. I do this by eating the food.
- I have to rewire my belief that in order to eat this type of food, I need to have moved extra that day. I do this by eating the food and not compulsively moving.
- I have to rewire the urge to compensate for eating this sort of meal by eating less elsewhere in the day. I do this by eating the food, and eating without restriction elsewhere in the day also.
- I have to rewire the belief that I am not the "type of person" who eats this sort of food. I do this by eating the food.
- I have to rewire the feelings of wrongdoing after eating this sort of food. I do this by refusing to engage with feelings of wrongdoing.

- I have to rewire the negative body image thoughts that are prone to emerge after eating this sort of food. I do this by eating the food and refusing to indulge in negative body image thoughts.

- I have to rewire the concept that I need permission from someone else to eat this sort of food. I do this by eating the food regardless of whether or not other people are also eating the food, or have told me to.

- I need to rewire the belief that this sort of food is "bad" or "unhealthy". I do this by eating the food, and refusing to engage in thoughts of judgement.

- I have to rewire my fear of eating "too much" of this sort of food if I allow myself to eat without restriction. I do this by eating without restriction and refusing to engage in thoughts and stories about negative consequences.

- I have to rewire the tendency to allow my judgement over this type of food to stop me from being truthful and admitting that I do want to eat it.

I could go on. You get the picture. This, all of it, is exactly why when someone is put on a meal plan and told not to "overeat" in recovery, they will struggle to achieve full recovery. Eating without restriction enables rewiring to happen. So much rewiring! Any sort of restriction, even that with the best of intentions such as a meal plan, can be an obstacle to nutritional rehabilitation and neural rewiring.

Unrestricted eating teaches us the lifelong skill, blessing, of being able to listen to and trust one's own body. This skill can only emerge when we rewire the distrust of our bodies and judgement of food that having an eating disorder creates.

REWIRING FOOD JUDGEMENT (LEARNING TO EAT HONESTLY)

There is one major obstacle that many of us have when we try to eat without restriction. We have been believing our own stories about the type of food that we like for so long that the truth can be difficult to find.

Years of believing that there are "good" and "bad" foods, and that I was a person who didn't like the "bad" foods, meant that I had many layers of food judgement and a slight identity crisis to work through before I could fully understand what unrestricted eating even meant for me.

I had to accept that it was not true that I didn't like pizza and burgers and fries. I liked these foods very much. The fact that I didn't like that I liked these foods didn't make it any less true that I wanted to eat them — and in large quantities. I deeply wanted to eat all the foods I was scared of eating in quantities that terrified me.

The rewiring here involved stopping believing the stories that I had been telling myself (aided and abetted by diet culture, of course) about these types of food. It also involved training myself out of the idea that there was virtue in food. I had to re-learn that food is … food. That is all. Not eating pizza didn't make me a better person. Restricting the very foods my body was asking me for and pretending I didn't want them was a form of dishonesty I had to address if I wanted full recovery. Because full recovery means learning to trust that if my body wants to eat something, that is truthful and innocent communication that I must listen to.

Learning to eat honestly was a process for me. Admitting to myself, and then others, that I did like the foods that for years I had been adamant I didn't was both terrifying and liberating. Terrifying because in doing so, I had taken down a wall protecting me from my ability and desire to eat. Liberating because in doing so, I had taken down a wall forbidding me from my ability and desire to eat.

Some of the skills I had to develop to eat truthfully were:

- The ability to intercept the hard-wired verbal *"no thank you"* response that would leave my lips when someone offered me a challenging food.
- The ability to regulate my nervous system with long, slow, deep breathing when I was embarking on eating a challenging food.
- The ability to rewire by ignoring my hard-wired distrust of any communication regarding food from my body, and to be able to continue eating past the amount that my disordered brain perceived as "too much."
- The ability to ask for help and support from other people by inviting them to accompany me as I went out to eat the challenging foods I was truly desiring (that's as simple as: *"Hey, want to go get fish and chips with me tonight?"*).

One of the steps in this mental unravelling for me was sitting with the question: *"Is that actually true?"*

It seems so simple, doesn't it? But I had been acting on untruths for so long that my hard-wired reactions often didn't give me time to consider what might be true. An example being that the words: *"No thank you"* would already be out of my mouth before I had really considered the question: *"Would you like a slice of cake?"*

Was *"No thank you"* actually true?

No! In almost all circumstances the answer was no, that was not true. Of course I wanted a slice of cake. I kid you not, it blew my mind a bit to realise that. I had been saying: *"No thank you"* for so long that I had believed it without ever questioning it. Baffling!

"No thank you" protected me from my desire. It made it so that I didn't even have to seek my desire. It made everything so simple. It was easy. Asking myself the question: *"Is that true?"* opened up so many complications and problems and freedom.

This can bring about a crisis of identity. I had built my internal picture of myself based on the lie that I was a person who didn't like pizza. That I wasn't the "sort" of person who ate fast food. That I was different than the masses, the cake-eaters. Turns out, I wasn't. I'm not. And thank God for that, because if enjoying cheeseburgers, beer, and having a life makes me common, I'll take it.

Often, learning to eat truthfully requires stepping out of the robotic set of responses that work so well to aid us in our re-striction. This step is absolutely necessary if you want any hope of being able to listen to the honest communications that your body is giving you about what you want, need and desire.

Your body is not a robot. Your body has desires. These desires are honest and innocent. Resisting these desires doesn't make you su-perior; resistance leads to an inferior experience of life. It leads to struggle, and is the opposite of health. I had to learn that true "health" is listening to my body, without judgement, before any-thing else.

Eating without judgement is a very crucial rewiring step for full recovery. For me, it shattered my perception of myself, and in doing so allowed me to relax into the person that I really am.

REWIRING COMPULSIVE MOVEMENT

Alright, now we're going to talk about a super-highway neural pathway!

Not every person with an eating disorder has the compulsive movement aspect. If you do, it will likely be your biggest rewiring challenge of recovery. The urge to move, and all the neural associations and learned behaviours that develop as a result of it, form a belief system that needs to be rewired. Belief systems are always the most difficult element to rewire, because beliefs are designed to be defended aggressively once established.

To recover fully from compulsive movement, we must rewire thoughts, actions, reactions, emotions and beliefs.

Let's take an example of the morning walk that a client of mine, Sally, would compulsively take herself on after eating breakfast. Not getting up and going on that walk after eating would threaten considerable anxiety. If she were to question whether or not she should go for a walk, her brain had a plethora of justifications as to why she should. The most common thoughts she could identify were: *"Everyone knows movement is healthy,"* and, *"At the treatment centre we would be allowed to walk after breakfast, therefore it must be okay."*

The second thought there, in particular, is one that is common for people who have been in treatment, and very convincing. I often hear from people in recovery who have been told at one point or another that their desire to walk is okay, and they don't have to try and counter it. Granted, that the same individual may have been told a hundred times since that they do need to stop walking to fully recover by different treatment professionals. But you can guess which story stands out strongest in their brain. Yes, the one that gave them permission to walk.

And this is because that story is the one that best aligns with her belief system that has grown over the years since Sally developed an eating disorder. Our brains are wonderful at taking only the information from the environment that supports our beliefs, and ignoring that which doesn't.

Now consider all the information in our society and culture that feeds the message that exercise is key to good health. Sally doesn't have to work very hard to find justification for her morning walk. And indeed, for a person without a movement compulsion, movement is far from harmful.

One of the biggest ongoing struggles I have is trying to convince treatment professionals who do not have direct lived experience with compulsive movement that to truly achieve full recovery, compulsive movement must stop. Even if a person is not at a dangerously low weight. Even if that compulsive movement is just a walk around the block. This is not so much about physical health as it is mental health and rewiring for full recovery.

Here is how Sally's life was affected by her compulsive morning walk:

- Breakfast always had to be eaten at the same time so she had time to walk before work.
- She always had to set her alarm 45 minutes early so she would have time to walk before work.
- She would never stay over at her boyfriend's house

because she would not be able to do her morning walk if she did.

- She would feel anxiety at having her boyfriend stay over at her house in case he didn't want to wake up as early as she did to do her walk.
- She would do her walk even if unwell.
- She would feel anxiety over going on holiday in case her morning walk was effected.
- If she had to be in work early for any reason, she would either wake herself up for her morning walk even earlier, or make sure she did it after work.
- She would feel anxiety around anything that interfered with her walk.

None of the things in this list will affect the number on the scale, by the way. All of them will affect Sally's ability to do what she wants with her life. This is about freedom, not weight.

The bigger aspect of this walk is that it was a super-highway providing energy to the whole neural network that made up her eating disorder. Therefore, while Sally was still going for that walk in the morning, it meant it was harder for her to be changing other things — like eating without restriction — as she was placing herself "in" her eating disorder neural network at 7am each morning with that walk.

I know a morning walk seems so harmless, but if it is a compulsion, it can really impact on a person's freedom. The mental juggling that happens if someone so much as suggests that you alter your morning is incredible. I remember how my brain would go off into a tailspin at even the thought of changing one of my movement habits. In the end, Sally would always say "no" to any deviations of her usual morning just to escape the anxiety of changing.

When I suggested to Sally in our consultation session that the morning walk had to go, she cried. I could tell for the rest of the session she was having trouble concentrating. Her mind was still mulling on the "no walking" thing — as mine would have done when I had anorexia. I was somewhat surprised when she booked another session the next week. So was she. She told me that after what I had said about her walking, she wasn't sure she could work with me. The fear of stopping was too much of an obstacle. I pointed out that if a 45-minute morning walk was all that was standing between her and the possibility of full recovery, the very fact that she was almost willing to hang on to that walk rather than fully recover was evidence enough of how problematic, and how deeply wired into her eating disorder, that walk really was. She already knew that, of course.

That's the thing with lived experience; it adds texture that science alone can't see. I'm aware that studies may show that movement after eating reduces anxiety for people with eating disorders. I want to laugh and bang my head against the table every time I hear that one. Of course it fucking lowers anxiety! So would purging. So would restriction. It lowers anxiety because it appeases the eating disorder neural network. You can't only look at theory when you are dealing with a mental health issue, it doesn't tell the whole story.

Deep down, those of us with compulsive movement problems know we should stop. But we can convince ourselves that we don't, and we can convince our treatment providers that we don't. Of all the behaviours that those of us with eating disorders must cease in order to recover, 95% of the time the movement is the one that people struggle with the most (if that person has compulsive movement, not all do). This is where the real bargaining, justifying and negotiating happens. Most of us will defend our right to move or exercise in a way that would have Johnnie Cochran applauding. We can downplay it. We can convince you that movement lowers our anxiety and motivates us to eat more. We can hide it completely. We can hide it in plain sight: *"I have to walk the dog, so it's not a compulsion, it is a necessity."*

It is a problem, and it will remain a problem regardless of how much a person nutritionally rehabilitates unless it is rewired. And how do you rewire a compulsion? You stop doing it. Opposite actions.

Movement compulsions also involve standing rather than sitting. I would feel anxiety over sitting for any period of time. I do think this is biologically instigated by the urge to migrate due to food scarcity, but regardless of the origin of the compulsion, we must stop it to fully recover.

It's not just about exercise, it's rewiring the tendency to always move

Compulsive exercise comes under the category of "fucking obvious stuff." Compulsive lower-level movement, standing, fidgeting, cleaning, etc., can be subtler. The more subtle a behaviour is, the harder it is to rewire because your own brain can make excuses for it, and other people don't see it and point it out so much.

One example of a subtle behaviour I had to rewire was my tendency to always opt for whatever action allowed for the most movement. This had become a hard-wired reaction much the same as the way opting for the lower calorie food was. In the moment, it felt like I was making a choice. That I wanted to opt for movement. With the hindsight of full recovery, I can see it was a compulsion, and one that I am very happy to no longer have influencing my free will.

Whatever you do, do not underestimate the impact of that daily walk around the block, your tendency to stand rather than sit, and your identity as someone who vacuums the floor every day. You don't need to do any of those things, and you can prove this to your brain by abstaining from them.

HOW LONG DOES REWIRING TAKE?

Longer than a couple of weeks, but less than a couple of years is about as specific as I can be about that.

The second you fully commit to something like stopping compulsive movement or unrestricted eating, your life will change. There are immediate results. You will instantly have more freedom, more time, more agency. But it can be a year or more before a neural network is completely forgotten.

Most people find with the super-highways like compulsive exercise and "healthy" eating that they have to be actively opposing these inclinations for months (maybe years in some cases) rather than weeks before the compulsions no longer present themselves. The risk is that by returning to exercise too soon, we wake the beast, and this sets off that whole eating disorder neural network, not just the movement piece.

I can't even count the number of clients who have started up on a bit of exercise too soon and then reported to me that they seemingly, out of nowhere, felt the urge to restrict food slightly again. Or that they suddenly began to recognise that familiar feeling of wanting to "eat healthier." It is no coincidence at all that this tends to happen after someone started up exercise again. That is exactly how neural networks work. Movement is associated with restriction and food rules and the action of starting exercise again has stirred up those associations. This is not your brain being broken. This is your brain doing exactly what it is supposed to do, and it just needs a while longer to rewire those strong connections between exercise and those undesirable eating-disorder-related thoughts and behaviors. Give it more time, and there will be a day when you can engage in exercise without your eating disorder neural network piping up again.

When that happens with my clients, I tell them that is their cue that it is too soon, and they need longer for those neural networks to become more forgotten. Luckily, your brain will give you plenty of red flags that you are returning to movement too soon by stirring up old eating disorder thoughts and inclinations. Be on the watch for these, and take them seriously. If more rest is needed, invest in it. It will be worth it in the long run.

Rewiring works. I often used to think that I was just "broken," and it was an incredible relief to realise that, actually, my brain was working perfectly and doing exactly what I had taught it to do, and that I had the power to teach it to react, think and believe differently. As do you. Your brain is a product of the thoughts that you pay attention to, and your actions. Your actions inform your brain and, in turn, inspire your thoughts and your beliefs. If you don't want to have an eating disorder anymore, the single most important piece of advice I can give you is to stop acting like you have an eating disorder.

"In the middle of teaching class, I got hungry. I had just had lunch and was meaning to have a snack in between classes (but that would not be for another 45 minutes). So since I was hungry and had two minutes to go to the bathroom, I went and had a snack. And that felt totally fine! No guilt!"

"When I was getting ready for bed I was looking in the mirror, and since I had just had dinner, my stomach was sticking out, and I said to my brain: "This is what you look like, it's fine." And then, it was fine. I was able to drop it and not dwell more on that."

Made in the USA
Columbia, SC
18 October 2021